1000
Things to
Color

Kirsteen Robson

Designed and illustrated by
Candice Whatmore, Kate Rimmer,
Laura Hammonds and Ruth Russell.

Which robot do you like best? Color it blue, then color five of the others.

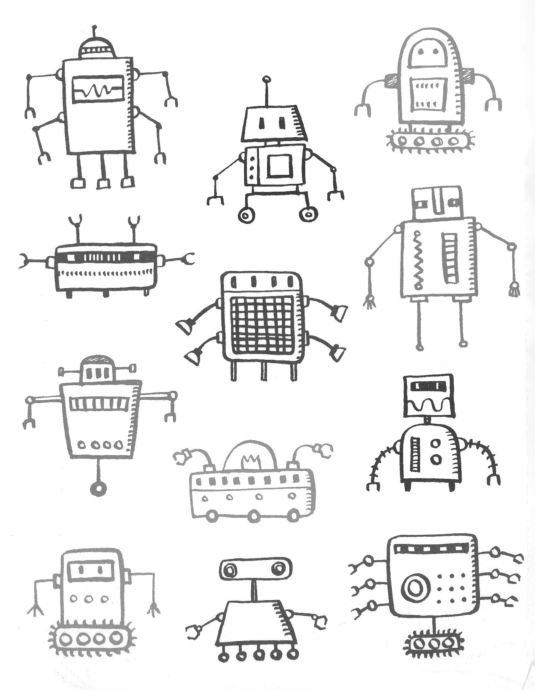

Color three spaceships and the six planets
and asteroids they hope to explore.

Brighten up eleven bags.

Find seven striped gifts and color them in.

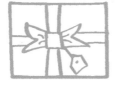

Color two creeping caterpillars and fourteen busy bugs.

Four plain watering cans need brightening up.

Finish coloring the nine yellow party flags.
Then choose two more to decorate.

Decorate six plain cupcake cases and color
five of the frosted flowers.

Choose fifteen vehicles and five other things to color.

Give seven smiling kitties
multi-colored coats to
be proud of.

Fill nine snazzy snail
shells with rainbow colors.

Make five of these tents stand out from the crowd.

5

Use your pens to turn nine
fish into tropical beauties.

Color six things the chefs are serving in this sumptuous feast.

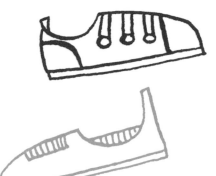

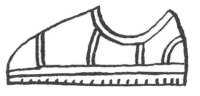

Color in ten shoes.

Fill in the spots and stripes to turn fifteen of these fading field mushrooms into funky fungi.

Color the five perching songbirds
and their leafy branches.

Fill in the tails of five little foxes.

Put the finishing touches on seven blankets, and color the two cactus plants.

Color five fresh fruits and five tasty vegetables.

It's a hot, sunny day. Give six sports spectators pink cheeks.

Triumph! Color six trophies, medals and ribbons to treasure.

Add a splash more color to each of these seven sailboats.

Use your pens to give these six
exotic birds fancy feathers.

Choose three scuttling crabs to color and three slimy seaweeds.

Add color to these mischievous monkeys so each one differs from its brothers and sisters.

Add patterns to brighten up seven tortoises.

Fill eight empty jars
with all kinds of
jellies, preserves
and pickles.

Give cold, wintery colors
to eight baubles and warm,
festive hues to another five.

Color in seven
kites shaped
like diamonds.

Fill in five flags and draw
emblems on four more.

Select seven skyscrapers and fill in as
many of their windows as you feel like.

Add patterns to eleven arrows and color in five more.

Brighten up ten of
these bouncing balls.

Choose colors for six of
these designer seats.

Find four matching flowers and color them differently.

Turn four apples into Rosy Russets and four more into Gardener's Goldens.

Color in eight piglets.

Decorate the four plain eggs
and color the geese
that laid them.

Cover five geckos with crazy patterns.

Use your colors to beautify
five fluttering butterflies.

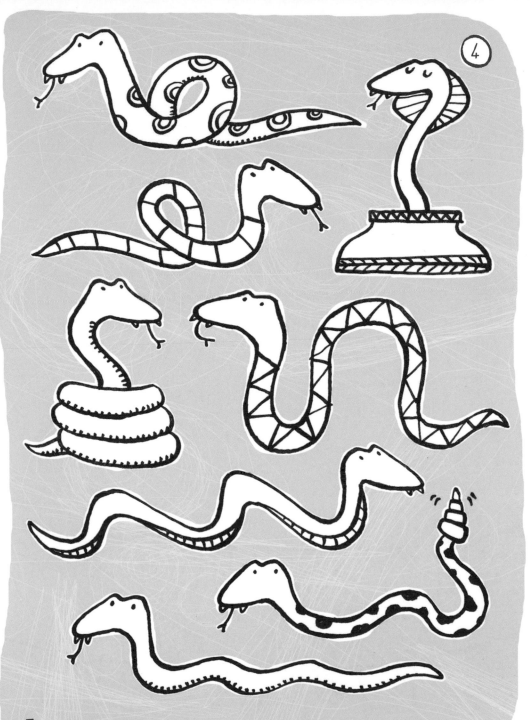

Four slithering snakes need spots, swirls and circles.

Find ten socks and make them into matching pairs.
Choose two T-shirts and cover them in stripes.

Choose six suitcases and use bright colors to make them easy to spot at the airport.

Use your pens to color sixteen snow-capped cottages and four pointed pine trees.

Cover fifteen floating jellyfish with spots, stripes, swirls and other eye-catching patterns.

Choose ten starfish and make
each one a different color.

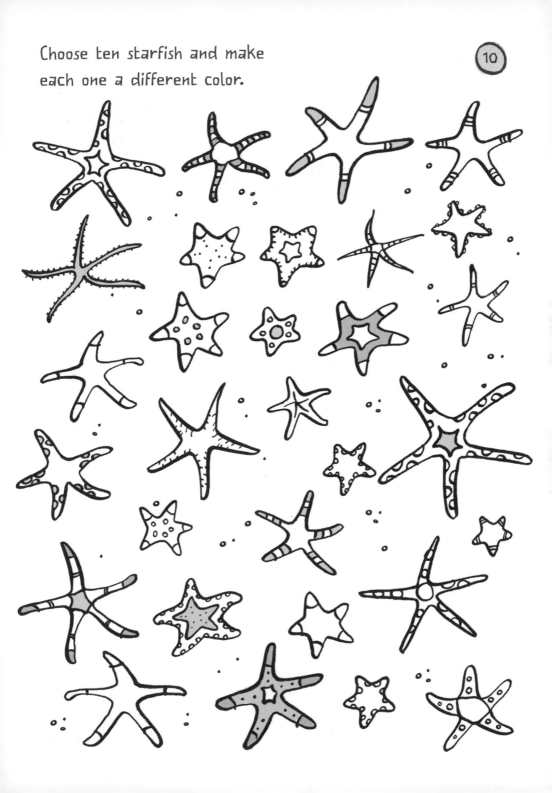

Will these five toothy terrors blend in with their swampy surroundings, or be spotted a mile away? You decide...

Color these elephants, decked out in their finery for a festive procession.

Choose twelve winning designs in this stamp competition 12 and use your colors to complete them.

Add patterns to the three
plainest pens or pencils.

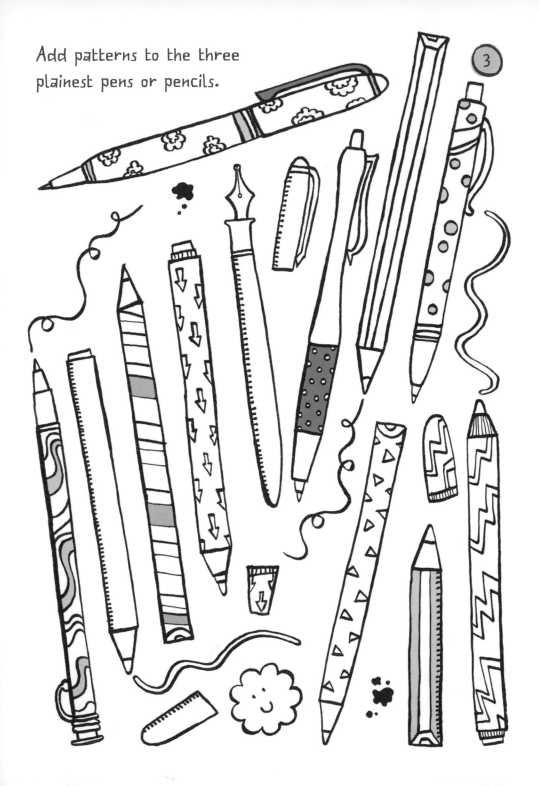

Give a new look to ten tired old lampshades.

Color four cushion covers.

Fill in five pictures and five frames.

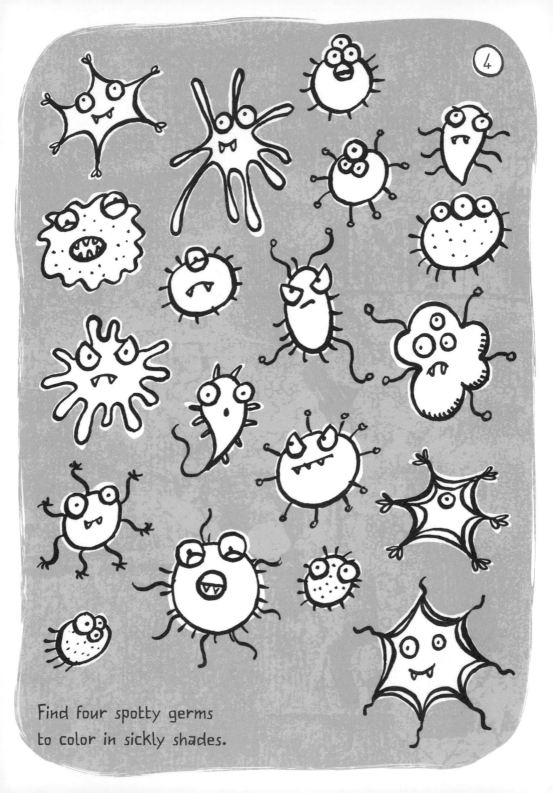

Find four spotty germs
to color in sickly shades.

Use reds, oranges, yellows and golds to fill
in the patterns on eight falling leaves.

Add color to four busy diggers and two trundling trucks.

Color twelve gloves and mittens
to make six matching pairs.

Add a personal touch to six winter hats.

Color the details on ten tall townhouses and six trees in the park.

Color the stripes on seven sports shirts...

...and design seven pairs of socks to match.

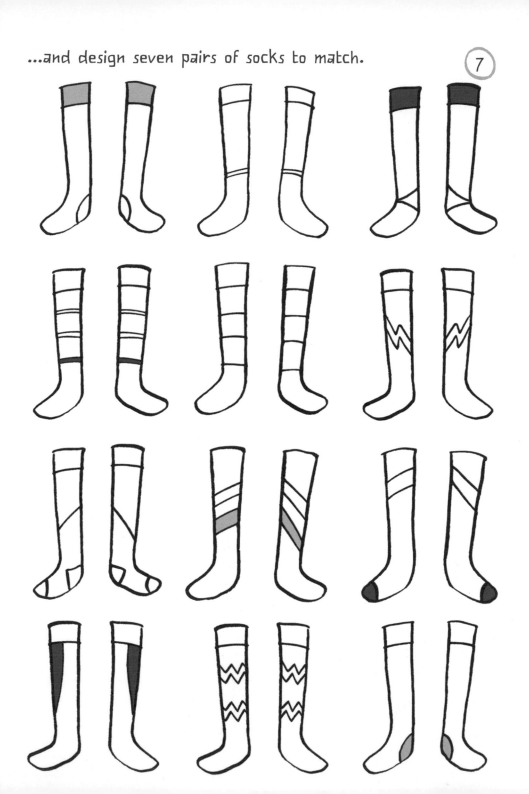

Give these six whirling windmills a fresh lick of paint.

Decorate the
parachutes.

Color the windows
and portholes on
ten bobbing boats.

Give ten turtles super-showy shells.

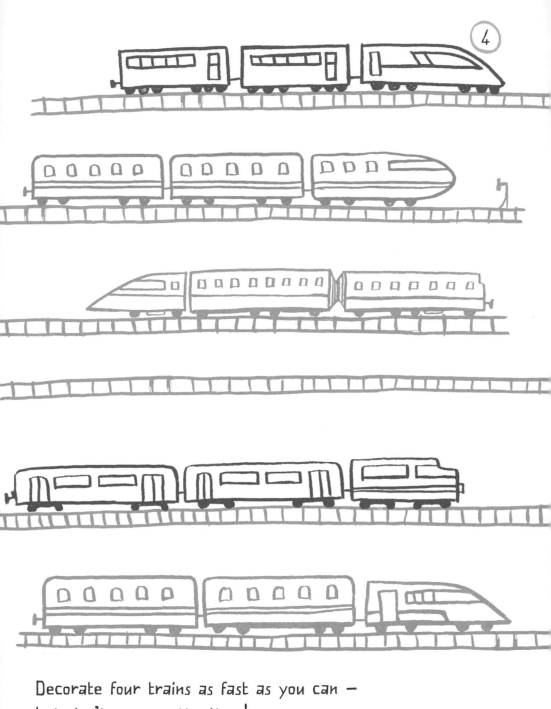

Decorate four trains as fast as you can —
but don't go over the lines!

Color five rackets and
five things to hit with them.

Give six skaters stylish sweaters.

6

Thirteen buzzing bees need yellow stripes.

Fill fourteen bottles and jars with brightly colored liquids.

Eighteen contented citizens are enjoying a sunny afternoon in the park. Pick something to color on each person.

Give sizzling shades to eight buckets and eight shovels.

Color ten tools you'd
like for your toolbox.

6

Color six splotches of paint and show which tubes they were squeezed from.

Fill in the details on ten
tasteless bow ties.

Color the decorations on nine novelty hairclips.

Add color to these
playful seahorses.

6

Give hats to five of the seagulls, and orange beaks to two more.

Shade in the stripes on the three kennels.
Decide which three dogs will live there
and color them too.

Turn seven smiling stars yellow and
fill in four patterned planets.

Add color to fifteen
fabulous rings.

15

Fill in three of these beaded bracelets.

Color seven buttons.

Brighten up five
floating balloons.

Use your pens to perk up
six purple caterpillars.

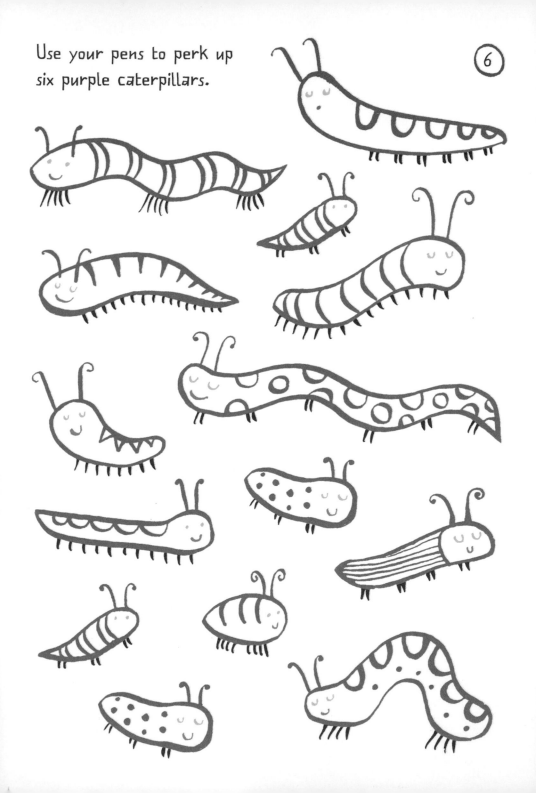

Draw patterns
on seven plain
plant pots.

7

Give eight owls a fine set of feathers.

Liven up the scenes in five of the windows.

Choose six creatures to color. Pick
whatever pens and patterns you like.

Color the stripes
and flashes on ten
trendy rollerskates.

Fill in the patterns on eight yo-yos.

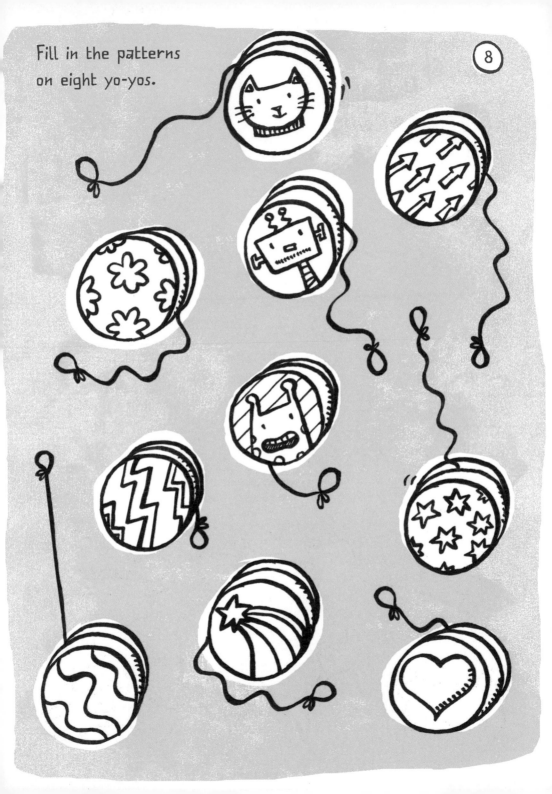

Fill in the details on
twelve costume hats.

Draw more patterns on
seven knitted scarves.

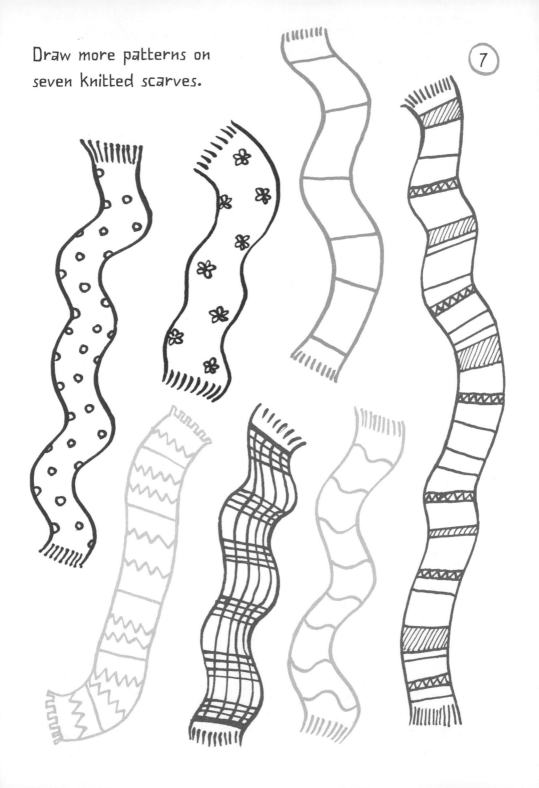

Shade in nine pairs of novelty shades.

Use your colors to create eleven irresistible popsicles.

Make sixteen candies look too tempting to resist.

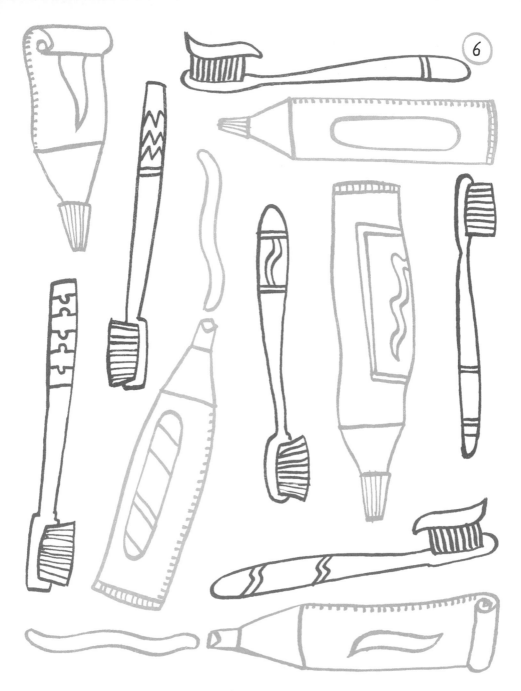

16

Design three terrific toothbrushes
and three toothpaste tubes to match.

Dress seven stagestruck penguins for a polar performance.

Draw watery patterns on
these diving dolphins.

Add designs bold enough
for planespotters to see.

Here are seven festival
balloons to finish.

Color two people and two animals,
and add leaves to three trees.

Choose twenty bugs and
beetles to color.

Color seven sensational sundaes, and eight other delicious desserts.

15

Create six cool
keytag designs.

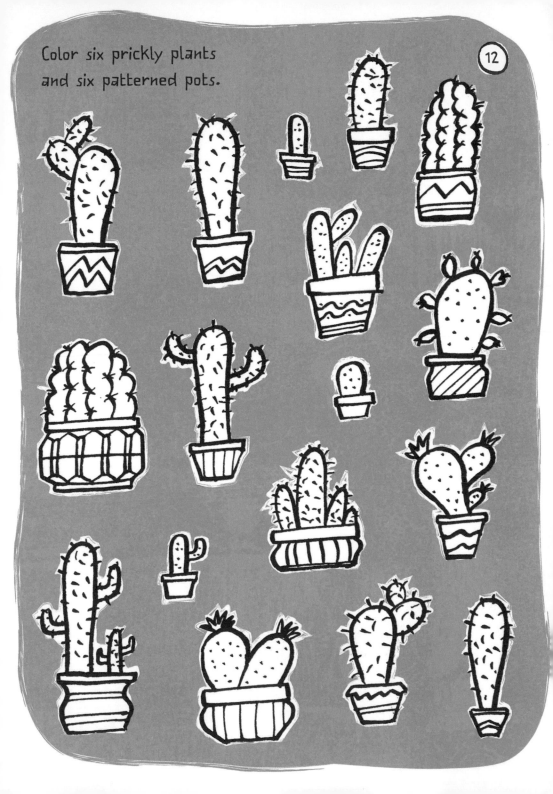

Color six prickly plants and six patterned pots.

Shade in seven spiral seashells.

7

Color in four
flamingos.

Finish the designs
on seven cups.

Add color to seven tempting cookies.

Color six umbrellas.

Use your colors to
bring to life ten
cuddly toys.

Add color to ten goggle-eyed monsters.

Make three thirsty
bats glow in the gloom.

Color six beach huts on the sandy shore.